THE STAR OF ILL-OMEN

LONDON.
MARCH, 1854.

WOULD Y'COP A LOAD O'THAT! AIN'T THAT A SIGHT AN' A HALF!

IT'S SO PRETTY...LIKE IT'S RAINING EMERALDS AND RUBIES! WHAT IS IT, JACK?

WELL, I UH...

ISSA DOOM, THAS WOT IT IS! I KNOW THESE FINGS! LIGHTS INNA SKY, ISSA ILL-OMEN, A JUDGEMENT ON ALL THE SINNERS, AN' ORES AN' PROCURERS!

GIVE OVER, MADGE! YOU DONE Y'FAIR SHARE O'SINNIN' IN Y'DAY. 'SIDES, AFTER ALL THE GIN AN' WALLOP YOU POUR DOWN Y'NECK, Y'CAN'T TELL Y'ARSE FROM Y'ELBOW HALF THE TIME!

IT'S LIKE A RAINBOW! A RAINBOW AT NIGHT!

ISSA SIGN! YOU MARK ME TRUE BY MY WHITE EYE!

THAT'S ENOUGH, YOU OLD BAG!

IT AIN'T ME AS SAYS SO... IT'S BEEN WRIT' IN TH'GOOD BOOK!

"AN' THE THIRD ANGEL SOUNDED AN' THERE FELL A GREAT STAR FROM THE 'EAVENS, BURNIN' AS IT WERE A LAMP...

"AN' IT FELL UPON A THIRD PART O' THE RIVERS AN' ON THE FOUNTAINS OF WATERS AN' THE NAME O' THE STAR WAS CALLED WORMWOOD.

"AN' THE THIRD PART O' THE WATERS BECAME WORMWOOD...

"AN' MANY MEN DIED O' THE WATERS, 'CAUSE THEY WAS MADE BITTER."

LONDON. AUGUST, 1854.

SHE'S GONE.

MAY THE GOOD LORD HAVE MERCY ON HER SOUL.

HER FAMILY WILL NEED TO BE INFORMED.

THERE ARE NONE. SHE WAS THE LAST.

THEN THAT MAKES ONE HUNDRED AND TWENTY SEVEN DEAD THUS FAR.

I FEAR HOWEVER, THAT THIS IS A GROSS UNDERESTIMATE. I SUSPECT THERE ARE MANY WHO TOOK TO THEIR ROOMS AND HOUSES SINCE THE OUTBREAK BEGAN AND HAVE NOT BEEN SEEN OR HEARD FROM SINCE.

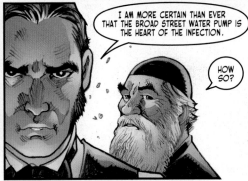

I AM MORE CERTAIN THAN EVER THAT THE BROAD STREET WATER PUMP IS THE HEART OF THE INFECTION.

HOW SO?

ASIATIC CHOLERA IS NOT SOME MYSTICAL MIASMA SPREAD THROUGH THE AIR, IT FESTERS AND PROPAGATES IN THE KIND OF CONDITIONS NOT A YARD FROM THIS OR ANY DOOR HEREABOUTS!

THERE ARE ANIMAL FAECES, GREASE-BOILING DENS, SLAUGHTERHOUSES AND A FETID SEA OF CESS-PITS. THAT SUCH A PESTILENCE SHOULD ERUPT IN THESE ENVIRONS WAS NOT A MATTER OF "IF" BUT "WHEN."

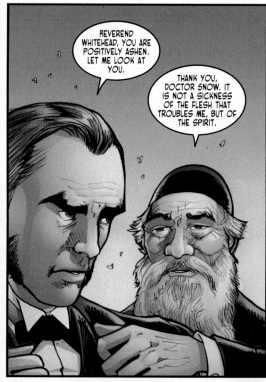

REVEREND WHITEHEAD, YOU ARE POSITIVELY ASHEN. LET ME LOOK AT YOU.

THANK YOU, DOCTOR SNOW. IT IS NOT A SICKNESS OF THE FLESH THAT TROUBLES ME, BUT OF THE SPIRIT.

YOU AND I HAVE BOTH SEEN THE DARKER SIDE OF HUMAN NATURE. YOU IN THE BODY AND I THE SOUL. I THOUGHT THERE WAS LITTLE LEFT TO DISTURB OR ALARM ME...HOWEVER I WAS WRONG.

SPEAK, MAN. WHAT IS IT?

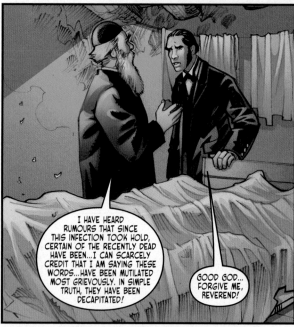

I HAVE HEARD RUMOURS THAT SINCE THIS INFECTION TOOK HOLD, CERTAIN OF THE RECENTLY DEAD HAVE BEEN...I CAN SCARCELY CREDIT THAT I AM SAYING THESE WORDS...HAVE BEEN MUTILATED MOST GRIEVOUSLY. IN SIMPLE TRUTH, THEY HAVE BEEN DECAPITATED!

GOOD GOD... FORGIVE ME, REVEREND!

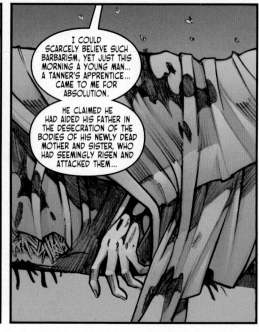

I COULD SCARCELY BELIEVE SUCH BARBARISM, YET JUST THIS MORNING A YOUNG MAN... A TANNER'S APPRENTICE... CAME TO ME FOR ABSOLUTION.

HE CLAIMED HE HAD AIDED HIS FATHER IN THE DESECRATION OF THE BODIES OF HIS NEWLY DEAD MOTHER AND SISTER, WHO HAD SEEMINGLY RISEN AND ATTACKED THEM...

I DID NOT TAKE HIM FOR MAD OR A MURDERER, BUT HE WAS CLEARLY WRETCHED WITH GUILT!

WHITEHEAD!

DEAR GOD IN HEAVEN!

IT CAN'T BE... I FELT HER PULSE CEASE! SHE WAS DEAD...

SHE WAS DEAD!

KKSSSAAA!

LONDON. AUGUST 1898.

"WELCOME, GENTLEMEN, WELCOME TO MY HOUSE!"

I GIVE NO NAME NOR ASK IT OF OTHERS. FEW OF THOSE WHO SEEK ME OUT ARE ADMITTED THROUGH MY DOORS. THAT YOU ARE HERE IS IN NO SMALL RECOGNITION TO THE POWER, WEALTH AND STATUS YOU WIELD.

I KNOW ALSO THAT SUCH MEN HAVE EQUALLY RAPACIOUS APPETITES. TRUST ME WHEN I SAY THIS HOUSE CATERS FOR TASTES BOTH DARK AND EXTREME!

WHAT IS DONE WITHIN THESE WALLS, REMAINS WITHIN THESE WALLS.

GOOD SHOW!

YOUR WILL SHALL BE DONE. YOUR EVERY SATISFACTION ATTENDED.

ALL THAT REMAINS IS FOR YOU TO TELL ME YOUR DESIRES...YOUR NEEDS...YOUR VICES...

...OPEN YOUR MIND TO ME!

SO THAT'S HOW IT'S DONE!

TELL ME YOUR SECRETS... TELL ME ALL!

NOW, WATSON! ALARUM!

SHERLOCK HOLMES!

YOUR NEMESIS, SIR! YOUR METHODS ARE FLAWED! I BROKE YOUR HOLD OVER THE RIGHT HONOURABLE TRELAWNEY. HOPE, YOU ARE UNDONE!

I HAVE YOU NOW! YIELD!

YOU HAVE EMBRACED ONLY YOUR OWN DEMISE!

THE WOLF DOES NOT YIELD TO THE LAMB!

UHH!

YOU ARE LOST, HOLMES. PAST HOPE. PAST SALVATION.

HHH...

HOW I HAVE LONGED FOR THIS MOMENT... TO FEEL MY HANDS AT YOUR THROAT!

GHKKK!

WHAT, NO LAST WORDS? NO FOND GOODBYES?

WHAT WAS THAT?

HSHHT!

...LIGHTS OUT!

I SAID...

BLAM
BLAM
BLAM

EXCELLENT MARKSMANSHIP, DEAR FELLOW, MOST COMMENDABLE.

ARE YOU HURT?

ONLY MY DIGNITY.

IT... IT'S A MACHINE?

AN AUTOMATA YET HOST TO THE KIND OF COMPACT, COMPUTATIONAL COMPLEXITY CHARLES BABBAGE COULD SCARCELY DREAM OF.

SEE HERE, THE DESIGN ON THE FLOOR IS INLAID WITH CONDUCTIVE COPPER. IT MUST BE HOW IT DREW IT'S POWER AND PERHAPS EVEN INSTRUCTIONS FROM ITS MASTER?

MASTER?

IT KNEW ME, WATSON. NOT JUST BY NAME. FROM THE WAY IT SPOKE, IT WAS AS IF IT KNEW ME PERSONALLY!

14

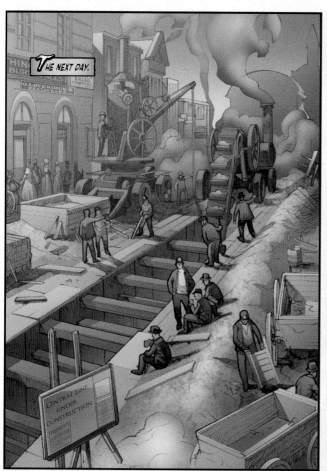

THE NEXT DAY.

GUH, STROLL ON! IT'S HOT ENOUGH T'BOIL CABBAGE DOWN HERE! WHY'S IT ALWAYS YOU AN' ME, EH? WHERE'S THE REST O'THEM JOKERS?

UP TOP HAVIN' A SMOKE AN' A BREW BY ALL ACCOUNTS.

OLD BLAKLEY SAYS IT DON'T NEED MORE'N TWO OF US T'STRING THE LIGHTS UP.

DON'T GET ME STARTED ON THAT INGRATE! FOREMAN MY ARSE. HE WOULDN'T KNOW HOW T'BREAK A SWEAT IF HE WORKED IN A BLEEDIN' BAKE HOUSE!

'ERE, WHAT'S THAT?

WHAT'S WHAT?

OVER THERE, SOMETHIN' SHININ'...

IT'S A RING!

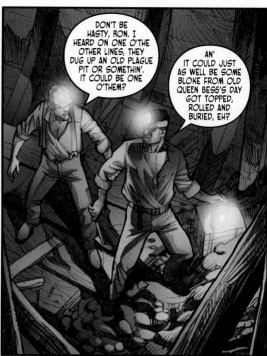

LET HIM BE, Y'BASTARD!

THWOK

IT'LL BE ALL RIGHT, MATE...I'LL GO GET YOU A DOCTOR, HE'LL PUT YOU RIGHT...YOU'LL BE RIGHT AS NINE-PENCE, YOU'LL SEE...

HHKK... UHHKK...UHH... GUHHH...

RON?

GHHK...

OH, STREWTH! YOU HAD ME GOIN' THERE FOR A MINUTE. I THOUGHT YOU'D KICKED--

YOU REALLY SHOULD SEE THIS, WATSON! THE DEGREE OF CRAFTSMANSHIP IS QUITE BREATHTAKING. I'D EVEN DARE TO CALL IT BEAUTIFUL!

NO...THANK YOU, HOLMES. I HAVE STOMACH ENOUGH FOR CONVENTIONAL AUTOPSIES, YET SOMEHOW I FIND THIS MORE... DISTURBING!

IT'S THOSE DAMNED EYES, THEY KEEP FOLLOWING ME AROUND THE ROOM!

THE WORLD OF THE AUTOMATA INVENTOR IS A UNIQUELY CONFINED ONE. THIS SURPASSES THE CREATIONS OF THE GREAT FATHER AND SON JAQUET-DROZ AND EVEN THE WHIMSICAL GENIUS OF JACQUES DE VAUCANSON.

I BELIEVE THE AMERICAN, EDISON, IS WORKING ON A TALKING DOLL--BUT IT IS NOTHING COMPARED TO THIS!

20

SCOTLAND YARD.

IT'S A CONUNDRUM TO BE SURE. AT FIRST, IT SEEMED LIKE A CUT-AND-DRIED CASE. TWO WORKMEN, COBBETT AND BAKER, ARGUED AND FOUGHT OVER A GOLD RING THEY'D FOUND.

IT CAME TO BLOWS...AND ENDED WITH COBBETT MURDERING BAKER.

COBBETT HIMSELF SUFFERED A NASTY SHOULDER WOUND...A BITE NO LESS. NOTHING SERIOUS, EXCEPT A COUPLE OF HOURS AGO, HE WAS GRIPPED BY A FEVER, TOOK A SEIZURE AND DIED.

THUS FAR, NOTHING I HAVE HEARD GREATLY DISTINGUISHES THIS INCIDENT FROM THE MYRIAD ACTS OF CRIMINALITY THAT UNFOLD IN THIS CITY ON A DAILY BASIS.

WHAT IS IT THAT MAKES THIS CASE AS DISTURBING AS YOU STATE?

SEE FOR YOURSELF...

MEET THE LATE DANIEL COBBETT!

GNAMM! GNAMHH!

I THOUGHT YOU SAID HE WAS DEAD?

HE WAS... HE IS... BUT HE WON'T LIE DOWN!

DON'T BE ABSURD! THIS MAN'S CLEARLY DERANGED, BUT NOT DECEASED!

DOCTOR, IF YOU'D BE SO KIND.

OF COURSE.

IT'S ALL RIGHT DOCTOR, HE'S WELL BOUND.

SNAMGH! GRAMPGH!

HE'S COLD. CLAMMY. NO BODY HEAT AT ALL AND... NO PULSE EITHER... BUT THAT'S IMPOSSIBLE!

AND YET HERE HE IS.

HOW CAN THIS BE?

ONE MINUTE HE'S GONE. NEXT, HE'S UP, SNAPPING AND SNARLING LIKE A TERRIER. LUCKILY WE GOT A BLANKET OVER HIS HEAD AND MANAGED TO RESTRAIN HIM.

WAS ANYONE HURT? SCRATCHED OR BITTEN?

NO, BUT THERE'S MORE. WE ALSO FOUND THIS AT THE SCENE.

FASCINATING!

IT WAS WITH BAKER AND COBBETT AT THE UNDERGROUND DIGGINGS. GOT HOLD OF ONE OF MY LADS' TROUSER CUFFS AND WOULDN'T LET GO!

GAAAR!

I EXPECT YOU'D LIKE TO VISIT THE SCENE OF THE CRIME?

INDEED I WOULD...

...HOWEVER, I BELIEVE THESE GENTLEMEN MAY HAVE SOMETHING TO SAY ON THE MATTER.

INSPECTOR LESTRADE?

I AM, AND WHO MIGHT--

READ THIS.

DON'T YOU TELL ME...

READ IT...

I...AH... I SEE...

YOUR SUPERIORS WILL BRIEF YOU SHORTLY. UNTIL THEN YOU'LL SPEAK OF THIS TO NO ONE, UNLESS YOU WANT TO SPEND THE REST OF YOUR DAYS IN UNIFORM, WALKING THE BEAT!

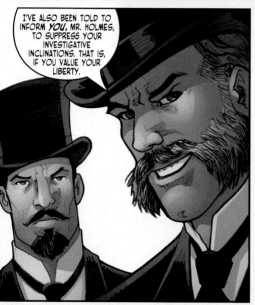

I'VE ALSO BEEN TOLD TO INFORM *YOU*, MR. HOLMES, TO SUPPRESS YOUR INVESTIGATIVE INCLINATIONS. THAT IS, IF YOU VALUE YOUR LIBERTY.

I SHALL GIVE IT DUE CONSIDERATION, THANK YOU.

NOW, ON YOUR WAY.

CURIOUSER AND CURIOUSER!

HOLMES? DO YOU KNOW THEM?

ONLY BY REPUTATION.

WATSON, WE HAVE JUST BEEN SHOWN THE DOOR BY AGENTS OF HER MAJESTY'S SECRET SERVICE!

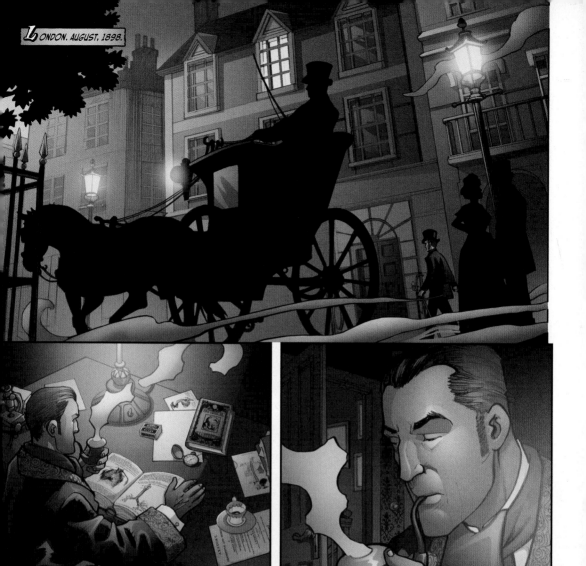

GOOD MORNING, WATSON! DO COME IN, THERE'S A FELLOW, INSTEAD OF LURKING ON THE LANDING LIKE A FOOTPAD!

I'M SORRY. I DIDN'T WANT TO DISTURB YOU, HOLMES.

YOU'RE NOT. YOUR COMPANY IS MOST WELCOME. BESIDES, THE LOOSE FLOORBOARD NEXT TO YOUR BED HERALDED YOUR VISIT SEVERAL MINUTES AGO.

THE SKULL BENEATH THE SKIN

YOU'VE BEEN UNABLE TO SLEEP, TOO, I TAKE IT?

NOT A WINK! I CLOSE MY EYES, ALL I CAN SEE IS THAT HORROR, GNASHING ITS TEETH!

AH, THE SCOTLAND YARD REVENANT. IT IS INDEED INTRIGUING!

THAT'S PUTTING IT MILDLY! THE MAN WAS DEAD, HOLMES. I'D STAKE MY REPUTATION ON IT!

HE HAD NO PULSE. HIS FLESH WAS COLD AND PALLID. I ALSO GLIMPSED DARK PATCHES WHERE LIVIDITY HAD SET IN, THE BLOOD SETTLING AND POOLING AS HAPPENS WHEN THE HEART CEASES BEATING.

EVEN THE EYES AND MOUTH WERE DEVOID OF NATURAL MOISTURE. THAT WRETCHED CREATURE WAS A CORPSE, PURE AND SIMPLE.

OF THAT, I HAVE NO DOUBT. I WAS ACTUALLY REFERRING TO OUR BEING DISMISSED BY AGENTS OF HER MAJESTY'S SECRET SERVICE.

THEIR SUDDEN AND SWIFT ARRIVAL WAS NOT BY CHANCE, THE IMPLICATION BEING THEY ARE SOMEHOW INVOLVED IN THIS, THOUGH TO WHAT DEGREE IS UNCLEAR.

THEY ALSO WARNED YOU TO KEEP YOUR DISTANCE... UNDER THREAT OF IMPRISONMENT!

PRECISELY! AN UNDULY HEAVY-HANDED APPROACH THAT ONCE AGAIN IMPLIES THEIR COMPLICITY!

WE'RE GOING TO VENTURE INTO THAT HELLISH HOLE IN THE GROUND, AREN'T WE?

WHAT GIVES YOU THAT IDEA?

BECAUSE I KNOW YOU. YOU'D PROBABLY MADE YOUR MIND UP BEFORE I'D EVEN ENTERED THE ROOM.

HOW, PRAY TELL, DID YOU REACH THAT CONCLUSION?

BY USING YOUR OWN DEDUCTIVE SKILLS!

I NOTE YOU'VE ALREADY BATHED, SHAVED AND DRESSED, SINCE IF I AM NOT MISTAKEN NIGHTSHIRTS DO NOT COME WITH FRENCH CUFFS AND CUFFLINKS!

VERY GOOD... BUT WHERE IS YOUR EVIDENCE FOR THIS HYPOTHETICAL EXCURSION?

I'M RESTING MY FOOT ON IT. THE BAG OF TOOLS, BENEATH THE TABLE!

"FOR IF WE ARE TO PLAY THE RESURRECTIONIST, I FEAR IT WILL NOT BE WITHOUT HAZARD."

FORGIVE THE IMPERTINENCE, HOLMES, BUT WE'VE BEEN DOWN HERE ALMOST AN HOUR. DO YOU KNOW WHERE YOU'RE GOING?

OF COURSE. WERE IT NOT THAT WE HAD TO CIRCUMVENT THE SENTINELS ON THE SURFACE, IT WOULD HAVE TAKEN US A MATTER OF MINUTES TO GET HERE.

AS IT IS, WE HAVE HAD TO COME THE LONG WAY AROUND.

THESE TUNNELS AND CORRIDORS RUN PARALLEL WITH THE UNDERGROUND LINES AND STATIONS. THEY PERMIT ARMIES OF ENGINEERS TO GO ABOUT THEIR WORK UNIMPEDED, WITHOUT INCONVENIENCING THE PUBLIC...

THIS INDUSTRIOUS UNDERWORLD IS HOST TO KITCHENS AND BUNK HOUSES, WORKSHOPS AND EVEN A HOSPITAL.

I NEVER KNEW THIS PLACE EXISTED!

FEW DO... FEWER STILL KNOW THE ENTIRE LAYOUT.

AND YOU DO?

IF SUCH KNOWLEDGE IS OF USE TO THE CRIMINAL FRATERNITY, THEN IT IS OF INTEREST TO ME ALSO!

AH, HERE WE ARE! IT'S LAMPS FROM HERE ON IN.

IT'S QUITE A STEP. MIND THE GAP!

THIS IS WHERE THE MAIN WORKINGS WERE BEING UNDERTAKEN...

THEN DOWN THERE MUST BE WHERE COBBETT AND BAKER MET THEIR MONSTER!

YES, THERE... SEE, WATSON? THE EARTH HAS BEEN DISTURBED, PUSHED UP FROM BENEATH. THIS IS WHERE THEIR ATTACKER SPRANG FROM.

It is... it's a mass grave!

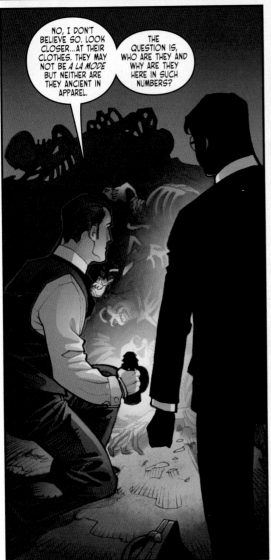

No, I don't believe so. Look closer...at their clothes. They may not be *a la mode* but neither are they ancient in apparel.

The question is, who are they and why are they here in such numbers?

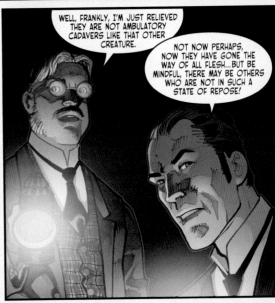

Well, frankly, I'm just relieved they are not ambulatory cadavers like that other creature.

Not now perhaps, now they have gone the way of all flesh...but be mindful, there may be others who are not in such a state of repose!

There's a postman here...and he still has his satchel!

THERE'S POST IN IT!

THESE LETTERS, THEY'RE DATED LAST JULY? BARELY A YEAR AGO. HOW ON EARTH DID THEY COME TO BE HERE?

AH!

KKSSSAAA!

GNAMSH GHAMPH!

NNGH!

UNHAND HIM, YOU FIEND!

GLAARGG!

SHUNKTT

MY GOD... MY GOD...

STEEL YOUR NERVES, DOCTOR. I FEAR WE ARE NOT DONE YET. DID YOU BRING THE VERY PISTOL?

UH, YES... YES I DID.

MWWUHHHH!

FETCH IT, MAN, HURRY!

BDAMFF

DEAR GOD IN HEAVEN!

I FEAR IT IS SAFE TO SAY THAT THE ALMIGHTY HAS NO PLACE HERE, MY FRIEND...

OVER THERE, GO!

THERE'S NO BLOODY STOPPING THEM!

BLAM BLAM

AIM FOR THE HEAD, THAT SEEMS TO HAVE THE DESIRED EFFECT!

SLUCH

I'M OUT OF AMMUNITION!

GO ON, I'LL KEEP YOU COVERED!

BLAM
CLICK

BRAMM

IT DEPENDS ON WHO'S LISTENING!

THE FLARE... IT'S GOING OUT!

STEADY, OLD FRIEND, STEADY.

PAMFF

PAMFF

BAMFF

WHERE DID... WHAT THE DEUCE?

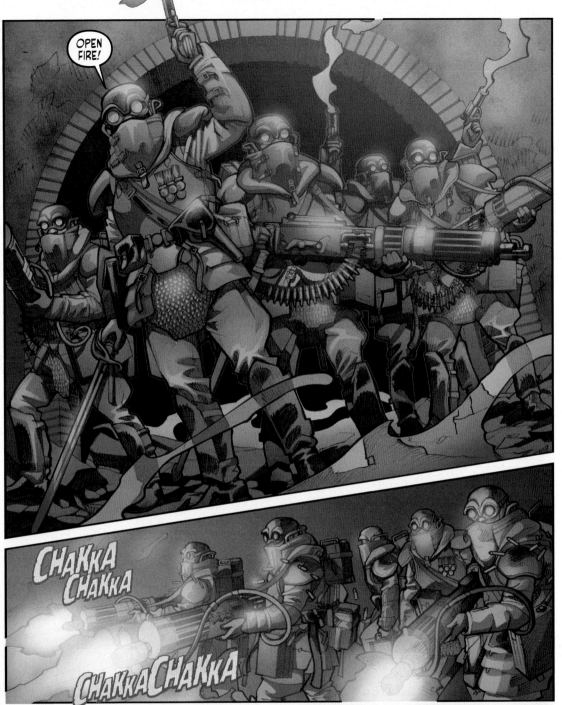

OPEN FIRE!

CHAKKA CHAKKA

CHAKKACHAKKA

POK SPLIKK SPLAKK

YOU KNEW ABOUT THEM?

I.... SUSPECTED.

I AM NOT A MAN INCLINED FOR ACTION AND ENDEAVOUR, AS YOU WELL KNOW, YET I HAVE FORSAKEN A GOOD BOOK, A LARGE BRANDY AND A WARM BED TO SNATCH YOU BOTH FROM A GHASTLY DEMISE!

A LITTLE CONSIDERATION WOULD NOT GO AMISS!

I APOLOGISE FOR INCONVENIENCING YOU, MYCROFT, HOWEVER, YOUR INTERVENTION WAS MOST TIMELY AND APPRECIATED.

YES, INDEED!

HMM... YES, WELL COME ALONG.

I DARE SAY IT'S TIME FOR EXPLANATIONS ALL 'ROUND BUT FIRST, BREAKFAST!

DOES THIS MEAN WE'RE NOT GOING TO JAIL THEN?

NO, DEAR FELLOW--

"--THE DIOGENES CLUB!"

WELL NOW, COLONEL. WHAT NEWS OF THE LAND OF THE LIVING?

THE PLAN PROCEEDS APACE. HOWEVER... THE CENTRAL LINE CACHE, IT... WAS DISCOVERED PREMATURELY AND DESTROYED BY THE ARMY. I'M SORRY, PROFESSOR.

I SEE... AND HOLMES?

WAS PRESENT, AS YOU SUSPECTED, IN THE COMPANY OF HIS CORPULENT BROTHER AND THAT BORE, WATSON! IF I'D HAD MY RIFLE I'D HAVE CULLED THEM ALL!

I ADMIRE YOUR ZEAL, SEBASTIAN, BUT WITHIN FORTY-EIGHT HOURS HOLMES AND HIS ILK WILL NO LONGER BE OF ANY CONCERN TO US.

BUT THE CACHE...

IS OF NO CONSEQUENCE, A MINOR INCONVENIENCE, NOTHING MORE. AFTER ALL, THAT IS THE BEAUTY OF BEING ABLE TO CALL UPON AN ARMY OF THE DEAD...

WRITTEN IN BLOOD

London. August, 1898.

THE DIOGENES CLUB

AH, KIDNEYS AND KEDGEREE, SPLENDID!

I MUST SAY, THE UNGODLY HOUR ASIDE, THIS MORNING'S ENTERPRISE HAS GIVEN ME QUITE AN APPETITE!

WILL SIR BE DINING?

THANK YOU, NO. COFFEE WILL SUFFICE.

SIR?

UH, NO. NOTHING FOR ME, THANK YOU.

YOU LOOK A LITTLE GREEN ABOUT THE GILLS, DOCTOR. AS BOTH A PHYSICIAN AND A PROFESSIONAL SOLDIER, I ALWAYS TOOK YOU TO BE MADE OF STERNER STUFF.

DO NOT MISTAKE MY DISCOMFORT FOR COWARDICE, SIR. I HAVE ENDURED MY SHARE OF BLOOD AND HORROR, BOTH IN SERVICE TO THIS COUNTRY AND IN YOUR BROTHER'S COMPANY.

I KNOW DEATH. I HAVE SEEN MEN DIE BEFORE ME...

HAVING THEM RISE AND ATTEMPT TO TEAR OUT MY THROAT HOWEVER, IS A WHOLLY NEW AND UNNERVING EXPERIENCE. ONE I WOULD DARE ANY MAN TO TREAT LIGHTLY!

FORGIVE ME, I MEANT YOU NO DISSERVICE. I FORGET MY MANNERS. RECENT MATTERS HAVE MADE ME RATHER...CURT OF LATE.

51

SUCH AS THE HORDE OF CANNIBALISTIC CADAVERS AT LARGE BENEATH THE CITY?

WHICH IS WHY, I ASSUME, DOCTOR WATSON AND I WERE THREATENED WITH INCARCERATION IF WE DID NOT KEEP OUR DISTANCE?

THE LATTER WAS BEYOND EVEN MY CONTROL. THE INCIDENT WITH THE UNDERGROUND WORKERS STIRRED UP A VERITABLE HORNETS' NEST IN CERTAIN QUARTERS.

HEAVY HANDS WERE AT PLAY WHEN A DEFTNESS OF TOUCH WAS REQUIRED INSTEAD.

FORTUNATELY FOR US, YOU KNEW I WOULD NOT HEED SUCH DEMANDS AND HAD US WATCHED ACCORDINGLY.

I WOULD HAVE BEEN SORELY REMISS IF I DID NOT.

TO THE MEAT OF IT, THEN... AND THE MARROW. THOSE CREATURES, HOW DID THEY COME TO BE?

HOW INDEED?

TELL ME, DOCTOR. ARE YOU FAMILIAR WITH THE WORK OF DOCTOR JOHN SNOW AND THE REVEREND HENRY WHITEHEAD?

OF COURSE! ANY PHYSICIAN WORTH HIS SALT KNOWS OF THEM.

DOCTOR SNOW WAS FOREMOST IN THE ADOPTION OF MEASURED SURGICAL ANAESTHESIA AND THE STRINGENT APPLICATION OF MEDICAL HYGIENE.

MOST NOTABLY HOWEVER, HE WAS A PIONEER IN THE THEN FLEDGLING FIELD OF EPIDEMIOLOGY AND GERM THEORY.

"HE WAS A VIGOROUS SKEPTIC OF THE MIASMA THEORY--THAT DISEASE WAS SPREAD BY FOUL AIR OR NOXIOUS SMELLS.

"HE TURNED THIS ON ITS HEAD WHEN HE SUCCEEDED IN TRACING AN OUTBREAK OF CHOLERA TO A SPECIFIC, POLLUTED WATER SOURCE."

THE BROAD STREET PUMP IN SOHO.

YES, THAT'S IT!

IT WAS THE SUMMER OF 1854 IF I'M NOT MISTAKEN.

HE DIDN'T TRUST ONLY TO THE MEDICAL SCIENCE BUT EMPLOYED DETAILED STATISTICAL AND DEMOGRAPHIC ANALYSIS IN STUDYING THE PATTERNS OF INFECTION.

SNOW CONFIRMED THE LINK BETWEEN THE OUTBREAK AND A WATER COMPANY THAT WAS SUPPLYING THE NEIGHBOURHOOD WITH SEWAGE-CORRUPTED WATER FROM THE THAMES.

AND THE REVEREND WHITEHEAD?

A CURATE AT ST. LUKE'S CHURCH. HIS LOCAL KNOWLEDGE WAS INVALUABLE IN PIN-POINTING THE OUTBREAKS AND ULTIMATELY THEIR SOURCE.

HM, A COMPETENT PIECE OF DETECTIVE WORK.

IT WAS NO MERE INTELLECTUAL EXERCISE, HOLMES, OVER SIX HUNDRED PEOPLE PERISHED.

ACTUALLY, IT WAS CLOSER TO FIFTEEN HUNDRED.

FIFTEEN HUNDRED! THAT WASN'T REPORTED AT THE TIME!

ALONG, I SUSPECT, WITH A GOOD MANY OTHER THINGS. IS THAT NOT SO, MYCROFT?

INDEED.

THOSE WHO DIED, ROSE AND PREYED UPON THE LIVING, SPREADING THE CONTAGION WITH EVERY BITE.

HOWEVER, IGNORANCE WAS THE GREATEST ENEMY...

"THE POLICE, SENT IN TO QUELL WHAT THEY THOUGHT WAS RIOTOUS, DRUNKEN MOBBERY, WERE SAVAGED AND SLAUGHTERED. SO TOO WERE THOSE WHO FOLLOWED.

"THE INFECTION THREATENED TO SPREAD EXPONENTIALLY.

"ONCE AGAIN, IT WAS THE GOOD DOCTOR SNOW, HAVING ENCOUNTERED THIS TERROR FIRSTHAND, WHO POSITED A PRACTICAL TACTIC.

HOW DID THEY BECOME INFECTED? WHERE DID THEY COME FROM? HOW CAN SO MANY PEOPLE GO MISSING WITHOUT A TRACE?

DO YOU KNOW HOW MANY PEOPLE VANISH FROM LONDON'S STREETS EACH YEAR?

I SHUDDER TO THINK.

THIS CITY HAS AN APPETITE ALL ITS OWN. IT IS LIKE THE GOD SATURN CONSUMING HIS CHILDREN.

IT WAS ONLY BY GOOD FORTUNE THAT ONE OF THOSE FLITCHES ESCAPED ITS CONFINES...

GOOD FORTUNE! HOW CAN YOU SAY THAT?

BECAUSE IF IT HADN'T, WE WOULD NOT HAVE FOUND THE REST! A MONSTROUS REGIMENT OF RAVENOUS CORPSES WHO WERE CLEARLY CREATED AND CORRALLED FOR A PURPOSE!

GOOD GOD...BUT...BUT WHO WOULD DO SUCH A THING? AND WHY?

FAIR QUESTIONS INDEED, BUT THERE IS ANOTHER WHICH IS THE MORE PRESSING...

WHICH IS?

"WAS THAT THE SOLE CACHE, OR ARE THERE MORE?"

THE TIME IS ALMOST AT HAND SEBASTIAN.

AND SOON WE SHALL PLAY OURS!

SNAPP

THE CITY STIRS, ITS VEINS AND ARTERIES ALREADY PULSING, THICK WITH LIFE!

A MYRIAD MUNDANE SOULS, THE GREAT SWELL OF HUMANITY HERE IN THIS HEART OF EMPIRE, TORPID WITH ITS OWN ARROGANCE AND VANITY!

IT THINKS ITSELF VAST...UNTOUCHABLE... ETERNAL...BUT I SHALL REACQUAINT THIS CITY...THIS NATION WITH A SENSATION TO WHICH IT HAD LONG THOUGHT ITSELF IMMUNE...I SHALL TEACH IT FEAR!

TING-TING-TING-TING-

THE HOUR IS STRUCK...

TING- TING- TING-

"NOW IT BEGINS..."

KDUNK
CLUNKACLUNKACLUN

CLUNKACLUNKACLUN

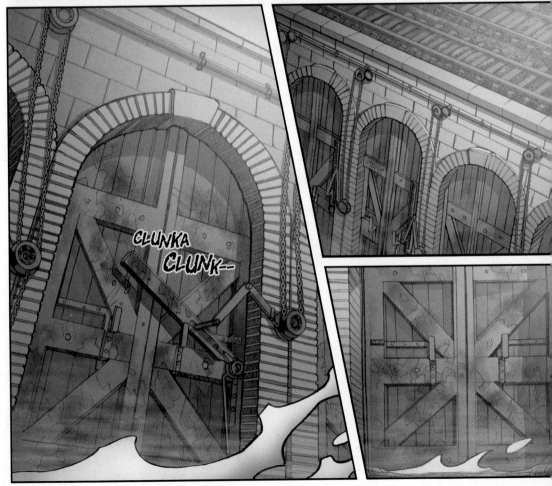

CLUNKA
CLUNK--

KREEK-K

MMHHHH...

MWWUHHHH!

KKAHH!

MWUHHH!

LATER.

HOLMES...
HOLMES...

HOLMES!

YES! WHAT IS IT?

YOU'VE NOT HEARD A WORD I'VE SAID THIS PAST TWENTY MINUTES, HAVE YOU?

I'M SORRY, DEAR FELLOW. MY MIND WAS INDEED ELSEWHERE.

AND NOWHERE GOOD AT THAT, I'LL WARRANT. YOU'VE HAD A FACE LIKE THUNDER SINCE WE LEFT THE DIOGENES CLUB!

IT'S THIS MATTER WITH MYCROFT. HE HAS A FIERCE AND ELEGANT INTELLECT, YET HIS HANDS ARE CLEARLY BOUND BY THE WHITEHALL MANDARINS TO WHOM HE ANSWERS.

A MIND OF HIS QUALITY SHOULD NOT BE TREATED SO. HE IS BEING SPOON-FED SNIPPETS WHEN HE SHOULD BE FURNISHED WITH THE WHOLE PICTURE!

THEY ARE GOVERNED BY PARANOIA AND RIGID WITH INERTIA.

DO YOU IMAGINE IF WE HAD NOT VENTURED UNDERGROUND THAT THEY WOULD HAVE DONE SO? THAT ANY OF THIS WOULD HAVE COME TO LIGHT?

GAAHH! GET AWAY!

HOLMES!

AWAY I SAID, BLAST YOU!

UHT!

DID YOU SEE THAT? THE BLACKGUARD TRIED TO BITE ME!

76 J. LION

WHAT THE DEVIL'S YOUR GAME, EH?

ONS & CO

GREENLEES
CLAYMORE
RARE OLD
SCOTCH

ENOS FRUIT SALT

GHLAARR...

OH MY LORD!

63

GET OUTTA TH' ROAD! STEP ASIDE!!

SNAPP
KRAKK

SCRUNCH
KRUNCH

WHAT'RE YOU DOING, MAN? I HAVE TO...

WAIT! WAIT!

GKKK...

KKKKK...

KKSSSAAA!

UHH!

GLKLL!

SEE, THERE'S MORE OF THEM.

MWWUHHH

WE HAVE TO DO SOMETHING!

WE SHALL... WE WILL...

"...BUT THIS MATTER IS BEST SERVED BY OUR SWIFT RETURN TO BAKER STREET!"

HOLMES, THIS BLOOD'S FRESH!

THE DOOR'S LOCKED!

GET AWAY WITH YOU!

BLAM BLAM BLAM BLAM

MRS. HUDSON, IT'S US! MISTER HOLMES AND DOCTOR WATSON!

IS...IS IT REALLY YOU?

IN THE PINK! SO PLEASE PUT THE PISTOL DOWN AND OPEN THE DOOR.

AS QUICK AS YOU CAN, MRS. HUDSON, WE HAVE COMPANY!

IN YOU COME, GENTLEMEN. BEST FOOT FORWARD!

GHHUUU

NHHUHH!

OH, MISTER HOLMES! I'VE HAD SUCH A TIME! THE POOR BAKER'S BOY...IT WAS BARELY AN HOUR GONE...HE WAS BRINGING MY ORDER WHEN...WHEN HE WAS SET ABOUT...

THDD THUNN

...I THOUGHT IT WAS SOME ROUGHS. I...I WENT OUT TO GIVE THEM A HIDING WHEN I HEARD HIM START SCREAMING...

THEY WERE SAVAGE, BITING HIM... EATING HIM ALIVE. HE KEPT CRYING AND CALLING FOR HIS MOTHER...

...I RAN INSIDE ...GOT ONE OF YOUR GUNS, DOCTOR... BUT WHEN I CAME BACK THEY'D GONE.

THERE WAS JUST HIS BLOOD, EVERYWHERE...

...I SHOULD HAVE DONE MORE...I SHOULD HAVE STOPPED THEM.

DO NOT BERATE YOURSELF. YOU ARE AN EXCEEDINGLY BRAVE WOMAN...

WATSON...

IT'S ALL RIGHT. GO. DO WHAT YOU MUST. I'LL JOIN YOU WHEN I CAN.

COME ALONG, MRS. HUDSON. I THINK A STIFF BRANDY IS THE ORDER OF THE DAY AND YES, THAT IS MY MEDICAL OPINION.

1854!

WHERE? WHERE? *WHERE?*

I NEED MY BAG. I FEAR SHE NEEDS SOMETHING STRONGER THAN... GOOD GRIEF! WHAT'RE YOU DOING?

SEARCHING!

HAH! SEEK AND YE SHALL FIND!

WHAT IS IT?

THE LONDON GAZETTEER --AN ANNUAL, HISTORICAL CHRONICLE OF LIFE IN THE CAPITAL--

--FOR WHICH, READ A TEDIOUS CATALOGUE OF BIRTHS, MARRIAGES, DEATHS AND DEBUTANTE BALLS. BUT ONCE IN A WHILE THERE IS A GEM IN THE DROSS...

AH, HERE. LISTEN... MARCH THIRD, 1854...

"A FIERY COMET PASSED SO LOW IN THE SKY, ITS DIMENSIONS WERE CLEARLY VISIBLE TO THE NAKED EYE. ITS TAIL GLOWED AN UNEARTHLY GREEN AND VIOLET HUE, SHOWERING PARTS OF THE CITY IN A RAIN OF GLITTERING LIGHT."

69

I KNEW I'D HEARD THE DATE BEFORE! IT WAS SIX MONTHS BEFORE THE BROAD STREET PUMP OUTBREAK AND IN THE SAME VICINITY!

A COMET? ARE YOU SERIOUSLY IMPLYING THERE'S A CONNECTION?

LET US CONSULT ONE OF THE FOREMOST MINDS ON THE SUBJECT, SHALL WE?

WHO IS THAT, COPERNICUS? GALILEO? NEWTON?

PATIENCE, DOCTOR... HERE.

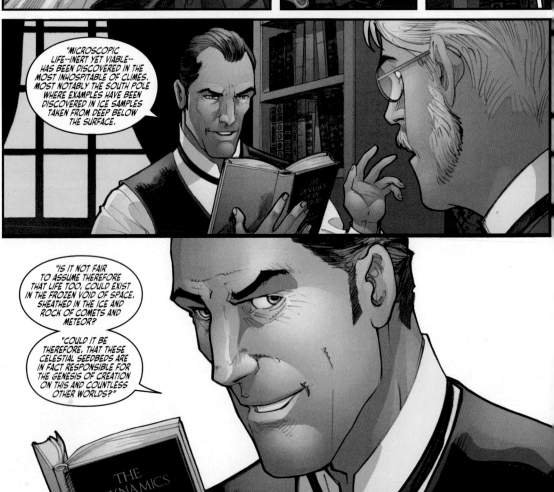

"MICROSCOPIC LIFE--INERT YET VIABLE-- HAS BEEN DISCOVERED IN THE MOST INHOSPITABLE OF CLIMES. MOST NOTABLY THE SOUTH POLE WHERE EXAMPLES HAVE BEEN DISCOVERED IN ICE SAMPLES TAKEN FROM DEEP BELOW THE SURFACE.

"IS IT NOT FAIR TO ASSUME THEREFORE THAT LIFE TOO, COULD EXIST IN THE FROZEN VOID OF SPACE, SHEATHED IN THE ICE AND ROCK OF COMETS AND METEOR?

"COULD IT BE THEREFORE, THAT THESE CELESTIAL SEEDBEDS ARE IN FACT RESPONSIBLE FOR THE GENESIS OF CREATION ON THIS AND COUNTLESS OTHER WORLDS?"

THE DYNAMICS OF AN ASTEROID BY

AND DEATH SHALL
HAVE NO DOMINION

PROFESSOR!

GOOD CHRIST!

GKKLLK... MH... MHORAN...

"I HAVE CHEATED DEATH!"

THREE YEARS LATER.

THE CAPITAL IS OVERRUN. ITS QUAILING POPULACE PENNED UP IN THEIR HOVELS, LIKE CATTLE AWAITING THE SLAUGHTER-MAN'S MALLET! THE CITY IS AS GOOD AS MINE!

WHEN YOU PUT YOUR TERMS TO THE GOVERNMENT, THEY'LL HAVE NO CHOICE BUT TO YIELD TO THEM.

TERMS? THERE ARE NO TERMS, COLONEL, FOR THERE IS NOTHING THEY HAVE THAT I SIMPLY CANNOT TAKE FROM THEM.

I DON'T UNDERSTAND. WHAT'S ALL THIS FOR, THEN?

IN MY FORMER LIFE, I HAD LITTLE IN THE WAY OF PHYSICAL LUSTS OR DESIRES. I HAVE LESS SO AS A CADAVER. MY CURRENT APPETITES ARE, SHALL WE SAY, SINGULARLY BASIC.

HOWEVER, NOW AS THEN, I DO STILL MAINTAIN ONE ALL-CONSUMING PASSION...THE ACQUISITION OF POWER! MY CIRCUMSTANCES MAY HAVE CHANGED, BUT MY AMBITION HAS NOT.

I AM IN THE UNIQUE POSITION OF HOLDING DOMINION OVER THE DEAD. THEREFORE, WHERE I WAS ONCE MERELY MASTER OF THE CRIMINAL UNDERWORLD, I NOW HAVE GRANDER DESIGNS...

...I SHALL MAKE THIS CITY MY NECROPOLIS AND FROM IT, I WILL FORGE AN EMPIRE OF THE DEAD UNTIL THIS ENTIRE WORLD IS MY HADES!

YOUR LOYAL SERVICE SHALL NOT GO UNREWARDED, SEBASTIAN. THE TIME HAS COME TO SHED THIS MORTAL COIL AND JOIN ME.

AS YOU WELL KNOW, THE SERUM--WHILE FATAL IN ITSELF--MUST BE ADMINISTERED WHILST THE SUBJECT STILL LIVES IF THEY ARE TO RETAIN THEIR CONSCIOUSNESS AFTER DEATH.

UH, PROFESSOR. I'D FOLLOW YOU IN MOST THINGS, BUT THIS...I CANNOT... I WILL NOT. IT...IT'S UNGODLY!

YOU DISAPPOINT ME, PLAYING THE DEATHBED HYPOCRITE AND EMBRACING THE ALMIGHTY AT THE ELEVENTH HOUR.

I SUGGEST THAT YOU RECONSIDER, AS THE ALTERNATIVE WOULD BE CONSIDERABLY MORE... UNPALATABLE!

85

I TRY TO PUT IT DOWN ON PAPER, TO MAKE SENSE OF IT ALL--BUT IT'S THOSE INFERNAL THINGS OUT THERE! THEY SHOULD NOT EXIST. THE DEAD DO NOT WALK. THEY CHAFE AGAINST LOGIC AND REASON! THEY DEFY SCIENCE!

ONLY SCIENCE AS WE KNOW IT. YOU'LL AGREE THERE IS ALWAYS MORE TO LEARN. AS FOR LOGIC AND REASON, I EMPATHISE, FOR I, TOO, FIND MYSELF STYMIED.

HOW SO?

THE PASSAGE OF THE COMET. THE FIRST RAISING OF THE DEAD. THE CACHE OF CANNIBALS. MORIARTY'S TREATISE. I CAN DRAW A LINE LINKING THEM ALL, YET IT WOULD ONLY BE CONJECTURE.

IT DEMANDS EVIDENCE AND INVESTIGATION, WHICH IS A SOMEWHAT TREACHEROUS PROSPECT AT PRESENT.

MISTER HOLMES, DOCTOR WATSON. LUNCHEON!

IT'S ONLY COLD CUTS AND LEFTOVERS, I'M AFRAID. THE GAS IS STILL OFF AND I'M SAVING THE OIL FOR THE LAMPS.

MRS. HUDSON, YOU ARE A WONDER!

YES, WELL. THIS IS THE LAST OF THE FRESH FOOD. IT'LL BE TINS AFTER THIS, WRETCHED THINGS.

I'M SURE IT WILL BE A CORNUCOPIA!

WHAT ON EARTH?

TINK TINK TINK

CHINKKA CHINKKA

THRAAMMMMMM

THRAAMMBBLLL

IT'S COMING FROM OUTSIDE!

HRR

SIR, COMPANY!

QUICK AS YOU CAN, MISTER HOLMES. WE DALLY TOO LONG AND THE FILTHY BUGGERS WILL BE ALL OVER US!

DOCTOR. MRS. HUDSON. IT'S TIME TO BE FLEET OF FOOT AND NIMBLE OF STRIDE. TAKE ONLY WHAT YOU CAN CARRY...

"...WE ARE LEAVING."

HOLMES... WAIT!

HOLMES!!

KGHRR! GHRAHH!

YYAHH!

NYHH!

CLUDTCH

IT'S COLONEL MORAN!

CAPTAIN, HELP HIM!

COVERING FIRE!

CHUDDA

CHUDDA

MORIARTY... HE'S ALIVE?

YES...NO... HE'S LIKE THEM...BUT HIS MIND IS WHOLE, EXCEPT...HE'S DERANGED.

WHAT DO YOU WANT WITH ME, MORAN? I DO NOT DEAL IN ABSOLUTION.

I AM A VILLAIN, SIR, BUT NOT A MONSTER. GREED CAN ONLY BLIND A MAN SO FAR.

NHGG...YOU MUST STOP HIM. HE WANTS TO BRING ALL TO FIRE AND RUIN, SIMPLY FOR HIS OWN SATISFACTION.

GHNN... HOLMES, I....I...

HE'S GONE.

NOT YET.

BLAM

GENTLEMEN, WE ARE LEAVING... NOW!

AT LEAST THERE WAS A SHRED OF HONOUR LEFT IN THE OLD "SHIKAR" AT THE END.

HE MIGHT HAVE AT LEAST TOLD YOU WHERE MORIARTY IS...

HE STILL CAN... AND MORE BESIDES.

COME, WATSON. THE GAME IS FINALLY AFOOT!

WINDSOR CASTLE.

WHY IS IT, WHEN ONE IS WAITING, TIME PASSES AT SUCH A GLACIAL PACE?

NO TIME IS EVER WASTED, WATSON. YOU MUST PUT SUCH INSTANCES TO EFFICIENT USE. TO EXERCISE THE MIND.

FOR EXAMPLE, OUR DELAY IS NO DOUBT DUE TO THE SUDDEN ARRIVAL OF THE DISHEVELLED LOOKING COURIER JUST PRIOR TO OUR APPOINTMENT.

THAT WE HAVE BEEN KEPT WAITING FOR ALMOST TWO HOURS SINCE SUGGESTS IT WAS NOT GOOD NEWS.

AT LEAST MRS. HUDSON IS SAFELY ON HER WAY TO HER SISTER IN INVERNESS AND WELL CLEAR OF THIS GHASTLY BUSINESS.

FOR NOW, DOCTOR... FOR NOW.

SHERLOCK, DOCTOR WATSON, THEY'RE ASKING FOR YOU.

99

I BELIEVE YOU ALREADY KNOW LORD BELLINGER.

PRIME MINISTER, A PLEASURE TO SEE YOU AGAIN.

MISTER HOLMES. DOCTOR WATSON.

GENTLEMEN, YOU HAVE BOTH BEEN OF DISCREET AND INESTIMABLE SERVICE TO THE CROWN ON SEVERAL OCCASIONS. THIS, HOWEVER, MAY BE YOUR MOST VITAL CALL TO DUTY YET.

WE ARE AT YOUR DISPOSAL, SIR.

YOUR BROTHER HAS INFORMED US OF YOUR INCREDIBLE DISCOVERY...OF THE MONSTROUS MACHINATIONS OF THE LATE PROFESSOR MORIARTY AND THE *"DEATHBED"* CONFESSION OF HIS CONFEDERATE, COLONEL MORAN...

IS THERE ANYTHING ELSE YOU CAN ADD?

ADD? MYCROFT KNOWS ALL THAT I DO--HE HAS MY ABSOLUTE CONFIDENCE. I HAVE KEPT NOTHING BACK...

WHY? WHAT HAS HAPPENED?

WHAT MANNER OF MAN WOULD YOU SAY MORIARTY IS?

ALIVE, HE WAS THE MOST DANGEROUS MAN IN BRITAIN. A VILLAIN OF CONSUMMATE GUILE AND CUNNING, COMPLETELY DEVOID OF MORALS OR MERCY.

WHAT HE IS NOW, I SHUDDER TO THINK, SAVE THAT IF HIS ACTIONS DROVE MORAN TO LEAVE HIS SIDE, IT DOES NOT BODE WELL...

NOW, PRIME MINISTER, I MUST PRESS THE QUESTION--WHAT HAS HAPPENED?

WE ARE LOSING LONDON, MISTER HOLMES. STREET BY STREET. OUR LINES ARE BEING OUTFLANKED, OVERWHELMED AND OVERRUN AT EVERY TURN.

THERE IS INDEED A FORMIDABLE MARTIAL MIND AT WORK HERE!

AS MYCROFT MADE YOU AWARE, THERE WAS ANOTHER SUCH OUTBREAK SOME FORTY YEARS AGO THAT WAS RESOLUTELY QUASHED.

YET YOU NEVERTHELESS ANTICIPATED ANOTHER, HENCE THOSE UNIQUELY ARMED AND ARMOURED MARINES AND THOSE QUITE EXTRAORDINARY VEHICLES!

THE TRUTH, SIR, IS DARKER THAN YOU THINK...

"DESPITE THE BEST EFFORTS, NEWS OF THE OCCURRENCE REACHED OUR ENEMIES OVERSEAS. THEIR AGENTS WERE DISCOVERED ATTEMPTING TO OBTAIN THE REMAINS OF THE INFECTED."

WHAT ON EARTH FOR?

TO USE AS A WEAPON!

IN THE MIDDLE AGES, IT WAS COMMON PRACTISE TO CATAPULT PLAGUE-RIDDEN CORPSES INTO WALLED CITIES UNDER SIEGE, IN ORDER TO INFECT THOSE WITHIN.

NOW, IMAGINE A HANDFUL OF THOSE CANNIBAL CADAVERS SMUGGLED INTO A CITY, THEIR BITES SPREADING THE INFECTION EXPONENTIALLY...

AND SUCH A FACILITY CURRENTLY LIES IN THE HANDS OF THE GREATEST CRIMINAL MIND OF THE AGE!

I CAN SCARCELY CREDIT I AM SAYING THIS--BUT CAN HE BE REASONED WITH?

NO. NOT THEN AND CERTAINLY NOT NOW.

DO YOUR TROOPS STILL HOLD THE CITY, DO YOU HAVE HIS FORCES CONTAINED?

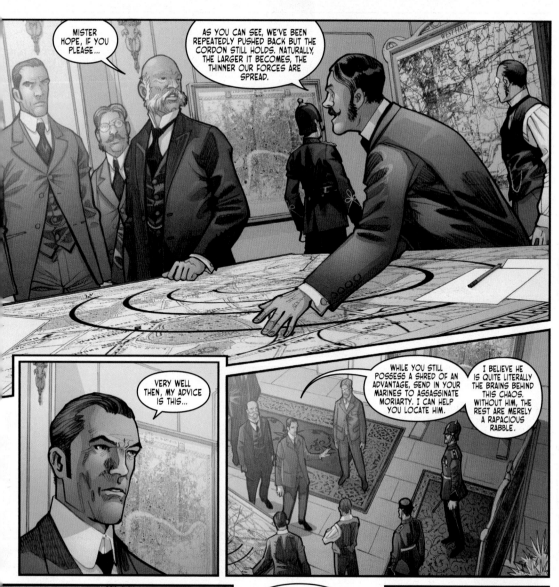

MISTER HOPE, IF YOU PLEASE...

AS YOU CAN SEE, WE'VE BEEN REPEATEDLY PUSHED BACK BUT THE CORDON STILL HOLDS. NATURALLY, THE LARGER IT BECOMES, THE THINNER OUR FORCES ARE SPREAD.

VERY WELL THEN, MY ADVICE IS THIS...

WHILE YOU STILL POSSESS A SHRED OF AN ADVANTAGE, SEND IN YOUR MARINES TO ASSASSINATE MORIARTY. I CAN HELP YOU LOCATE HIM.

I BELIEVE HE IS QUITE LITERALLY THE BRAINS BEHIND THIS CHAOS. WITHOUT HIM, THE REST ARE MERELY A RAPACIOUS RABBLE.

A RABBLE TENS OF THOUSANDS STRONG!

WHICH IS WHY YOU MUST THEN USE YOUR INCENDIARY WEAPONS TO CAUTERIZE EVERY SQUARE FOOT WITHIN THE CORDON.

YOU...YOU ARE SUGGESTING WE RAZE LONDON TO THE GROUND?

HOLMES, ARE YOU SERIOUS?

YOU MUST FACE THE FACTS, GENTLEMEN. THIS IS A FOE WHO NEVER SLEEPS, WHO KNOWS NEITHER PAIN NOR FEAR NOR INJURY, WHOSE RANKS SWELL WITH EVERY BITE AND TEAR.

WE MUST SACRIFICE THE CAPITAL TO SAVE THE COUNTRY. IF WE FALTER, BRITAIN WILL FALL AND THIS ISLAND WILL BECOME A FORTRESS OF THE RAVENOUS DEAD...HUNGRILY EYEING EUROPE AND THE REST OF THE WORLD.

NEVER MORE SO.

MISTER HOLMES...

LIKE IT OR NOT, SIR, YOU SOUGHT ME OUT AND THAT IS MY ADVICE.

COME, WATSON. WE HAVE WORK TO DO.

I DO NOT ENVY THE DECISION YOU HAVE TO MAKE BUT I URGE YOU TO DO SO SOONER, RATHER THAN LATER...FOR ALL OUR SAKES.

WESTMINSTER BRIDGE. LONDON.

GHRAHH!

KKSSSAAA!

HERE THEY COME...

...STAND BY YOUR GUNS.

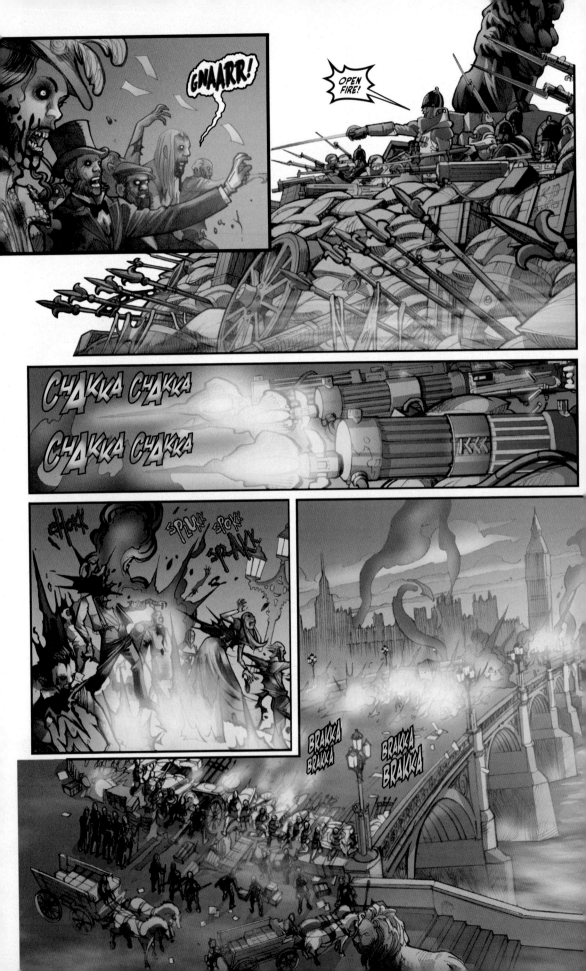

WINDSOR CASTLE.

HMPH...

PLEASE, WATSON. WORKING WITH THIS BORROWED EQUIPMENT IS TRIAL ENOUGH WITHOUT HAVING TO CONTEND WITH YOUR WITHERING GAZE AND GROWLS OF DISPLEASURE.

DISPLEASURE! HOLMES, YOU LECTURED THE PRIME MINISTER AS IF HE WERE A SCHOOLBOY, THEN WALKED OUT ON HIM!

I SIMPLY SAID ALL THERE WAS TO SAY. MY WORK THERE WAS DONE. MY WORK HERE IS NOT!

SHERLOCK, I HAVE GRAVE NEWS....

THE PERIMETER... IT HAS BEEN BREACHED?

AT WESTMINSTER BRIDGE. A DESPERATE REARGUARD ACTION IS BEING FOUGHT AS WE SPEAK. THE PRIME MINISTER HAS AUTHORISED YOUR PLAN... THERE WILL BE WARSHIPS ON THE THAMES BY DAWN.

AND MORIARTY?

IS TO BE LEFT TO BURN WITH THE REST.

GAH! WHAT IS THE POINT?! MY WORDS FALL ON DEAF EARS!

NOT ENTIRELY. I HAVE A FAST CARRIAGE WAITING AND A LAUNCH IDLING AT THE DOCK... THAT IS, IF YOU ARE GAME?

NOTHING IS CERTAIN, THAT IS WHY THERE IS STILL HOPE.

HOLMES, I... I WANT TO GO WITH YOU, BUT... I'M ASHAMED TO CONFESS... I... I'M AFRAID.

I AM GAME INDEED, BROTHER MINE!

COME, WATSON! WE ARE AWAY!

YOU... YOU MEAN TO GO BACK... INTO THAT ABATTOIR? IT IS CERTAIN DEATH!

MYCROFT, A QUESTION--I KNOW TRELAWNEY HOPE IS THE SECRETARY OF STATE FOR FOREIGN AFFAIRS--BUT WHY DID THE PRIME MINISTER DEFER TO HIM REGARDING THE TACTICAL DEPLOYMENTS?

IT IS A COVERT CONTINGENCY PLAN SHOULD LONDON EVER BE GRIPPED BY VIOLENT CIVIL UNREST. ANARCHISTS, SOCIALISTS, SUFFRAGETTES, THAT SORT OF THING.

IF A VITAL MINISTRY IS COMPROMISED, ITS POWERS ARE DEVOLVED TO ANOTHER.

WHEN THE HOME SECRETARY AND HIS STAFF WERE DEVOURED ON THEIR DOORSTEP, HIS POWERS OF OFFICE AUTOMATICALLY TRANSFERRED TO TRELAWNEY HOPE.

AND HOPE KNEW ABOUT THIS?

OF COURSE.

TELL ME, HOW EXACTLY TO YOU PROPOSE TO LOCATE MORIARTY? ONE CANNIBAL AMONGST THOUSANDS?

BY RETRACING COLONEL MORAN'S FOOTSTEPS...

113

YOU WERE RIGHT, HOLMES, THIS IS THE PLACE. HE WAS LIVING HERE!

AND MORE BESIDES, JUDGING BY THIS LABORATORY EQUIPMENT. MORAN WAS RIGHT, MORIARTY IS STILL IN POSSESSION OF AT LEAST SOME OF HIS FACULTIES.

HEADS... JUST HEADS. WHY?

COME NOW, MISTER HOLMES. SURELY THE GREAT DETECTIVE CAN WORK IT OUT?

GOOD GOD ALMIGHTY!

THAT WAS HIM?

YES, HE USED HIS MESMERIST MECHANICS ON THE RIGHT HONOURABLE TRELAWNEY HOPE, TO GLEAN THE CONTINGENCY PLANS SHOULD CIVIL UNREST OVERTAKE THE CAPITAL.

WE LITTLE SUSPECTED AN ARMY OF THE DEAD WAS WAITING IN THE WINGS TO EXPLOIT THEM.

ALL MEN WHO WIELD GREAT POWER HAVE APPETITES AND DESIRES TO MATCH. HOPE WAS NO DIFFERENT.

"HIS VICE MADE HIM VULNERABLE--

"--WHILE I PRIED HIS SECRETS FROM HIM USING A SIMPLE TRICK OF THE LIGHT!"

AND THAT WAS YOUR UNDOING! HOPE IS A METHODICAL MAN, WHO KEEPS HIS GOVERNMENTAL PAPERS IN STRICT ORDER.

"WHEN HE NOTICED THEM IN DISARRAY, HE SUSPECTED SOMETHING WAS AMISS AND SOUGHT MY ADVICE, LITTLE REALISING HE, HIMSELF, WAS THE CULPRIT."

IT TOOK NO SMALL EFFORT TO LOOSEN THE HOOKS YOU'D PLACED IN HIS MIND AND FREE HIM OF YOUR SKULDUGGERY!

BUT HOPE DIDN'T LEAD YOU HERE-- WHO WAS IT, MORAN? HOW DID MY JUDAS BETRAY ME? A TWINGE OF LATENT CONSCIENCE OR SOMETHING AS MUNDANE AS MUDDY FOOTWEAR?

A LITTLE OF BOTH, BUT COME SIR, WE ARE DONE WITH DISCOURSE! WE HAVE UNFINISHED BUSINESS AND NOT THIS PUPPETRY BUT FACE-TO-FACE!

NO... NOT ANYMORE. I AM REBORN...I HAVE REMADE MYSELF UPON THE LATHE OF THE HEAVENS. I AM A DEITY OF THE DEAD AND WILL MAKE THIS NATION, THIS WORLD, MY DOMINION.

YOU ARE AN INCONSEQUENTIAL THING TO ME NOW. FOR ALL YOUR IMPOTENT INTELLECT, YOU CANNOT CHANGE WHAT HAS HAPPENED NOR WILL HAPPEN.

121

KSSS!

HOLMES!

YOUR DEATH WILL MARK A BLOODY PUNCTUATION. THE CLOSE OF THE CHAPTER OF JAMES MORIARTY THE MAN--AND THE COMMENCEMENT OF MY REIGN AS MONARCH ETERNAL!

FEAR NOT, GENTLEMEN. YOU WILL NOT RETURN AS REVENANTS. I SHALL GRANT YOU THE BOON OF THE GRAVE, FOR IS THERE NOT MAJESTY IN MERCY?!

BLAMM

HE'S INSANE!

BLAMM

INDEED...

SHTASHH

GZHH!

AND NOW HE'S BLIND!

124

I SEE YOUR ENTERPRISE KNOWS NO BOUNDS. YOU REALLY ARE MOST IRKSOME.

I DO WHAT I CAN.

NEVERTHELESS, DO YOU HONESTLY IMAGINE YOU CAN STOP ME? THAT YOU ARE MORE THAN A MERE IRRITANT?

YOU CAN SLAUGHTER MY FOOT SOLDIERS BY THE THOUSAND--I CAN ALWAYS MAKE MORE.

THAT IS WHY I AM HERE!

YOU OVERESTIMATE YOUR CHANCES.

I AM NO LONGER PLAYING BY THE OLD RULES, DETECTIVE...

BDAMM

GAH!

132

133

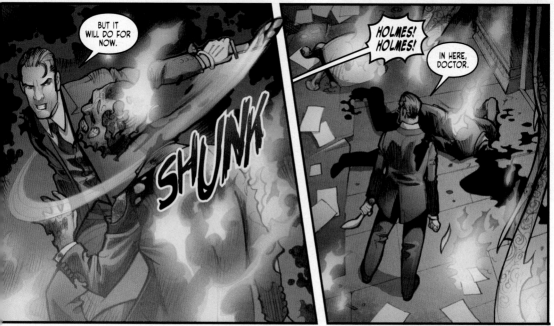

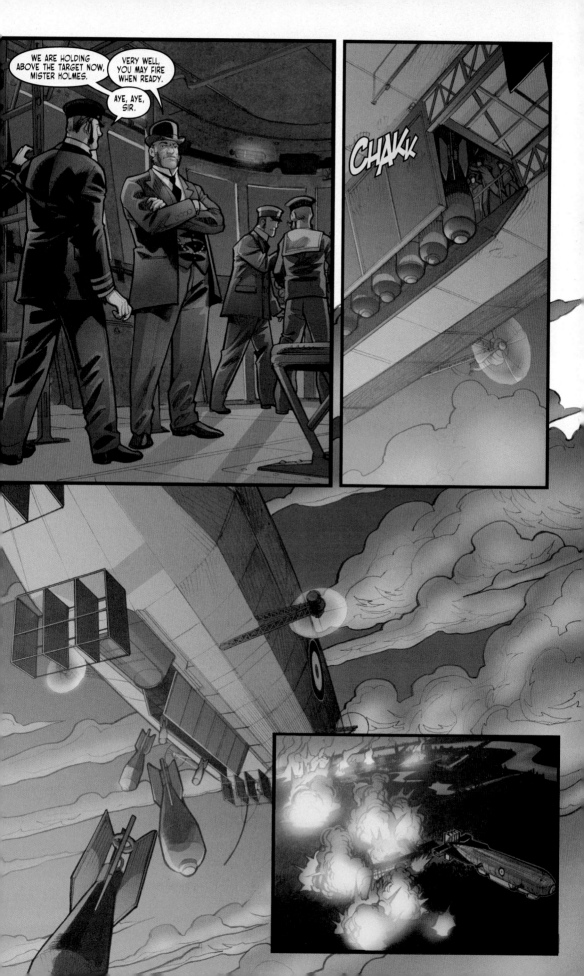

"SO BEGAN THE SECOND GREAT FIRE OF LONDON, WHICH, NOT UNLIKE ITS PREDECESSOR TWO CENTURIES BEFORE, SERVED TO PURGE THE TERRIBLE PLAGUE THAT AFFLICTED IT.

"EVEN THE THAMES ITSELF WAS SCOURED OF ANY LINGERING, LURKING HORRORS.

"THE COST HAD BEEN HIGH. THOUSANDS DEAD AND MILLENNIA OF RICH HISTORY SWEPT AWAY. YET LONDON, LIKE ITS PEOPLE, ENDURES.

"BARELY THREE MONTHS ON, RECONSTRUCTION HAS ALREADY BEGUN. A NEW METROPOLIS RISING FROM THE ASHES OF THE OLD."

WELL, WHAT DO YOU THINK? IT'S ONLY A ROUGH DRAFT, OF COURSE.

IT IS AS ELOQUENT AND ELEGIAC PIECE OF PROSE AS YOU HAVE EVER WRITTEN.

WHY, THANK YOU, HOLMES!

HOWEVER, SINCE WE WERE RECENTLY OBLIGED TO SIGN THE OFFICIAL SECRETS ACT, I DOUBT YOUR TALE IS LIKELY TO SEE PRINT.

AH...

NEVERTHELESS, YOU MUST FILE IT AWAY FOR POSTERITY. WHO KNOWS WHAT THE FUTURE MAY BRING?

A NEW HOME, FOR ONE...AT THE GOVERNMENT'S EXPENSE! IT WILL AT LEAST GO SOME WAY TO APPEASING MRS. HUDSON!

ACTUALLY, I WAS THINKING OF SOMETHING NOT QUITE SO PRAGMATIC.

WE ARE VENTURING INTO THE UNKNOWN, WE WHO SURVIVED THIS... CATACLYSM. OUR DESTINY FOREVER ALTERED BY EVENTS.